Collected Papers on Philosophy

*To the wonderful uniqueness
and complexity of our planet*

Perpend Publications

501

First printing November 2006

Perpend Publications
49 Chaucer Road
Rugby
Warks CV22 5RP

Printed by Cromwell Press Trowbridge

ISBN 10: 0-9553909-0-7
ISBN 13: 978-0-9553909-0-6

ii

Collected Papers on Philosophy

Considered Thoughts on Some Scientific Phenomena

J. W. Salmon, B.Sc.(Eng.), M.Sc.

Perpend Publications

CONTENTS

Philosophy Introduction

Philosophy could be defined as the search for knowledge, but this quest implies that the seeker has been motivated by the observation of some unusual or strange events and is inspired to undertake dedicated and patient investigations into the causes of such events, merely for the pleasure such knowledge can bring.

There are two kinds of event in which philosophers are mainly interested, namely those concerning human behaviour and those produced by natural phenomena. A philosophical pronouncement about the cause of a natural phenomenon can be – eventually – subjected to the scientific method of investigation, whereby repeated tests will establish the validity – or otherwise – of the pronouncement.

The investigation will often show that the pronouncement (which may be either a description of the relationship to known natural laws, or a statement about some hitherto unknown occurrence), may require modification to be applicable, but this does not obviate the value of the pronouncement.

An explanation of complex human experience or behaviour may be subject to many interpretations and reasoned arguments, but there is no scientific method for checking the truth of their conclusions. The conclusions may therefore be acted upon with either some degree of success or unfortunate results. The purpose of philosophy is here required to subject the explanation to critical examination and to describe what the actual cause(s) of the experience or behaviour may be. Subsequent action based on this philosophy should prove to be beneficial to mankind, but – beware – false doctrines will lead either to confusion or, at worst, to disaster. A guard against bogus doctrines is for the philosopher to have a true love of his subject and to receive no monetary or political gain from his research.

With this basis for philosophy the following descriptions are proffered for the purpose of either (eventual) scientific experiment or human approbation through beneficial experience.

Preface

These papers, now referred to as chapters, were previously transcribed onto the internet where – it is hoped – they reached a numerous and interested readership. However, owing to the transitory nature of a website, it was considered that a book of the collected papers would be of interest to a belated readership as well as to future generations. The aim has therefore been to convey the current thinking and practice, at the turn of the twenty-first century, on problems in scientific research on both human physiology and on astro and atomic physics. The chapters therefore convey my own efforts to understand the phenomena of the origin and shape of the universe and the nature of dreams, which – it is averred – are due to recent emotions experienced by a person. The remaining two chapters in the book are concerned with the fundamental particles produced by The Creation and the forces and energy that control the progress of physical events.

The philosophical thoughts that are conveyed in the book had puzzled me over a number of years, until I became convinced that some aspects of what had been published – particularly about the subjects of atomic and astro-physics – had serious flaws in their statements. For example it was propounded that all the material in the universe was created in a single instant, (the so-called big bang), and thereafter this material was projected radially outwards at high speed. All the material was therefore totally contained on the surface of an expanding bubble upon which the galaxies evolved, with empty spaces between the latter. This was clearly in conflict with the observation that the galaxies and stars exist at huge distances in every direction and fill the whole of space. I have therefore described an alternative hypothesis in chapter 1 for a continuous creation process, with eruption of matter in all directions, but with a gradual reduction in the eruptive intensity – i.e. in the material velocity – over the whole period of time since the initial Creation.

The observation that initially aroused my interest, and resulted in chapter 2, was made by the philosopher John Locke. He noted that the thought processes of some individuals became scattered, i.e. drastically disrupted, when they were either startled or encountered an event that – by association – induced a fear reaction. He gave no further consideration to the matter; but since it is not a rare occurrence I continually returned to the puzzle over many years and eventually came to the conclusion that human beings have many behavioural similarities with other animals. (This was at a time when human beings were thought to have been created differently – and were superior to – other animals). The human brain must therefore have a primitive – i.e. animal – part to its nature, which will memorise a situation that has induced fear; and this will always produce a similar response when a real, or imagined, associated danger occurs. It then became clear that – due to its greater intelligence than that of most other animals – the human brain must have evolved a separate mode for thought that can control its emotions. However, for extremely stressful situations, the control of the emotions induces a rapidly applied protective block to limit the fear response, which results in a traumatised state of mind. The protective block, however, can have a delayed response so that – when startled or confronted by a stressful situation – the individual can experience a fear reaction, associated with the trauma: this produces disrupted thinking and the animal instinctive reaction for flight.

This reasoning became combined with thoughts I had earlier about the nature of dreams, and how the latter were influenced by the emotions recently experienced by the brain. Having realised the importance of emotions – in every situation of daily life – and their links with images stored in the memory, it became clear that dreams were mainly due to a recall of emotional images recently stored in the memory. The recall of these images, however, are not accurately reproduced but are modified by the cortex, with either similar experience images or with communicated images from another individual. Some interpretation of a dream may therefore be necessary to discover its emotional content. This exercise can be self revealing and assists in the emotional development of the individual.

The process of learning is improved with the experiencing of pleasurable emotions during conscious activity; e.g. when achieving satisfaction in play or work; in acquiring genuine friendships and in education, hobbies and interests. Dreams are therefore important guides to the emotional satisfaction obtained with important aspects of living for the individual. Equally important they can warn the individual of an activity that is abhorrent to his/her nature.

The study, which led to the exposition of chapter 3, began with the divisions in scientific opinions at the beginning of the twentieth century about the ether. J.C. Maxwell – who had discovered the propagation of an electromagnetic wave through what he considered to be an ether (1864) – thought that there was probably more than one ether; although he was later persuaded that there might be only the one ether, (since there was no evidence, at the time, that gravity was associated with an ether). The Michelson -Morley Experiment (1887), then indicated that there was no variation in the velocity of light – through the supposed ether – when measured in different directions in space. They concluded that there was no velocity of an ether relative to that of the Earth, and that light was probably propagated through the vacuum of space. Einstein accepted this conclusion and based his Special and General Theories of Relativity on the assumption that the velocity of light was a constant throughout the universe.

It seemed to me, however, that the unit electrical charges, which J.C. Maxwell had conceived to be the carriers of electrical current through space, were one of the elements in an ether that could propagate his electromagnetic wave. There was another mysterious concept, used by M. Faraday in his study of magnetic fields, called lines of force; these seemed to be linked in some way with the same ether.

Unit magnetic poles, which were predicted to exist by P.A.M. Dirac but had not been discovered, were likely to form part of the same electromagnetic ether. Chapter 3 has therefore assumed that the electromagnetic ether does exist and has described its constituent particles, viz. the unit electrical charge and the unit magnetic pole. It therefore seemed reasonable to assume that there must also be a unit of mass, i.e. the fundamental particle of matter, which forms part of a gravity ether, and which has inspired physicists in the twentieth century to discover its existence.

I began a study for chapter 4 because it seemed to me – having read many of the books on the subject – that the scientists were unsure of the physics that was controlling events at the sub-atomic level. There were many speculations and theoretical attempts to draw the experimental results into a comprehensive theoretical framework; but there were obvious flaws in the latter, e.g. the QCD theory, which was failing to provide accurate solutions to the various problems.

When mathematics fails to provide accurate solutions it is a clear indication that the premises, on which it is based, are incorrect. I therefore began to speculate on the results of experiments from the large particle accelerators currently exploring the effects of collisions between particles.

The starting point was to assume that the unit mass, unit charge and unit magnetic pole, which were discussed in chapter 3, were present in a continuum of the ethers that controlled events both at the sub-atomic and macroscopic levels. This led to the speculation that the strong force was gravitational in essence, concomitant with the weak force being linked to the electromagnetic force (which had already been proven theoretically). However, the mathematics involved in the proof in the link, between the e.m. and the weak forces, was obtained using advanced mathematics and was not easily related to real physical effects. This required elementary particles to be defined in terms of the assumed fundamental particles of unit mass, unit charge and unit pole; e.g. it requires the electron to consist of three unit charge particles as well as a core of unit mass particles.

It followed that – if the fundamental particles are the unit mass, unit charge and unit magnetic pole – then they were produced by the process of creation and, like energy, cannot be annihilated. Further – if the energy of the electric and magnetic fields resides in the spaces between charged and magnetised bodies – then the energy associated with Einstein's formula, $E = m.c^2$, must be contained in the space surrounding a mass, not in the mass itself.

This led to the concept that the movement – or transfer – of energy must comprise the movement of fundamental units of mass, charge or magnetic poles along lines of force; and that the latter were due to associated particles, collectively referred to as potential energy particles (PEPs). The manner in which the unit particles are moved along or through the PEPs is not clear and the mechanism has not been defined in the book, but it seems likely that the PEPs form part of a separate entity, denoted as the omnific ether. This would indicate that energy in our universe forms part of – and may be influenced by – a much larger fount of energy in the omnific ether.

It then became clear that the earlier statements, when so-called anti-matter was discovered, that matter and anti-matter would be mutually annihilated – in a collision between the two particles – were therefore flawed. Since both these particles contain fundamental units of mass and charge, they cannot be annihilated; but can be merged into a combined mass of zero electric charge.

Similarly it became clear that the process of radio-activity was not a random occurrence; and the conversion of energy into matter, by the phenomenon of pair production, is not possible. Other suspect concepts have also been considered in the same chapter.

The chapters in this book are – in most part – the result of my own thoughts and understanding about the subjects of The Creation; dreams and human nature; and astro and atomic physics. They should therefore be appraised by the reader with due circumspection and with the realisation that a few corrections may be needed in the light of future scientific theories and experiments.

I am grateful to Mr. D.W. Cooper for the preparation of the text, both for its presentation on the internet and its subsequent rearrangement for publication in book form; and to Mr R.E. Cooper for assistance and advice with the presentation during the rapid advances made in computer technology during the writing of the text.

Thanks and appreciation are also due to Mr K.M. Pearce for the scrutiny and proof reading of all the texts and for his many suggestions, and much valued comments, made during long discussions that followed each completed chapter of the text.

CHAPTER 1

The Origin, Shape and Dynamics of the Universe

1. Before the Creation of the Universe an infinitely large space existed, which was structured with dark matter, the latter being an inherently stable medium.

2. A unique event then occurred at one singularity in this 3-dimensional space that produced an enormous temperature, which caused the creation – i.e. gigantic release – of the fundamental particles. These fundamental particles are the basic building blocks of matter, from which all elementary particles and their atoms are formed.

3. Due to the high temperature the fundamental particles exploded outwards in a spherical wave front. The amount of matter in the wave front was relatively small and its expansion took place without impedance from the surrounding dark matter. The fundamental particles had either zero or very small mass so that their initial velocities were either equal to, or approached, the speed of light.

4. As the wave front expanded it gradually cooled and the fundamental particles coalesced into elementary

particles, viz. quarks and leptons. Eventually the elementary particles combined into divisible matter, viz. baryons and mesons; further cooling then enabled atoms of hydrogen to form, from which clouds of turbulent gas came into existence and stars were subsequently formed.

5. When the wave front was forced outwards by the high temperature at the origin of Creation the temperature at the latter point began to decrease. Successive spherical shells of particles were therefore ejected at progressively lower velocities as time increased from the creation datum of zero. The fall in temperature at the origin was linear with time, hence the velocities of the expanding shells decreased linearly with time.

6. The outpouring of the fundamental particles from the origin continued over millions of years, but eventually the origin cooled to the level where the fundamental particles could combine into elementary particles as they were ejected. After many more millions of years the temperature was sufficiently low for particles of matter to be ejected. Eventually the temperature had cooled to the level where atoms of hydrogen were forming part of the spherical shells. The origin then began to generate heat by nuclear fusion, in the manner of star formation. The amount of heat generated, however, was less than that lost to the ejected elementary particles and gas.

7. This theory suggests that the origin of the Creation of our universe has not yet cooled to a level where no further matter is being ejected. It is suggested therefore that this origin is at the site of the brightest star in the universe, viz. that star which was recently discovered within our own galaxy.

8. An obvious conclusion of the theory is that our universe is spherical in shape with the greatest velocity of

the fundamental particles at its wave front and with slowest moving matter close to the origin.

9. Our Earth is relatively close to the origin, i.e. in the Milky Way galaxy, and the light reaching it from the most distant parts of the universe emanates from the earliest forms of ejected matter that could produce photons.

10. Due to the almost uniform density of matter at each spherical shell, of incremental thickness dr and radius r, light travels approximately linearly through the universe towards the centre. Light emitted in directions other than radially will travel in curved paths and will eventually be absorbed by other stars, gas or interstellar dust. Therefore an observer at the central origin (or near to it), will see only one object emitting light from a particular source.

11. Any light reaching the origin will be absorbed by the hot gas of the latter. The source of photons will emit light with a red shift (as is well known), dependent on the velocity of the source.

12. An observer at the Earth may therefore only view the furthermost matter in the universe after the photons from the latter have taken millions of years to reach the Earth. That furthermost matter will have taken a somewhat greater time to reach that distance from the origin as its photons subsequently take to reach the Earth. It is therefore apparent that the universe is (or is approximately), twice as old as that calculated from the light-years to the furthermost matter from the Earth.

13. The cooling of the wave front and successive shells, as described in paragraphs 4 and 5, is due to the energy conversion from kinetic to mass energy as the original fundamental particles gradually coalesce into elementary and matter particles.

14. This hypothesis of the dynamics of the universe suggests that the latter has evolved more in the manner of a gradual eruption, rather than from one initial big bang with all the matter contained within the wave front.

15. If, therefore, gravitational forces are insufficient to stop the expansion of the universe, as we view it at the present time, then – because there is a gradual diminution of matter being produced at the origin – the gravitational pull at the wave front is probably diminishing and the universe will continue to expand indefinitely.

16. It is also clear that the universe, as observed from the centre (and to a close approximation from the Earth), is uniquely seen to be expanding uniformly in all directions. For an observer at any large distance from the centre the velocities of the furthest objects would be different in various directions.

17. It is well known that the stars we are observing at the present time will have evolved further along their evolutionary paths than their appearance indicates. They may have progressed to become supernovae, turned into pulsars, collapsed into black holes, etc., but the myriad births of new stars causes the firmament to appear substantially unchanged; in reality, however, the average density of matter in the expanding universe will gradually diminish over aeons of time.

18. The background low level radiation, which can be detected in every direction in space, and which has been conjectured to emanate from a big bang, must have been emitted from elementary particles at the outer regions of the universe. The wavelength of this radiation (allowing for its enhancement by the red shift), is an indication of the temperature of these particles. Since the distance of these particles from the origin can be estimated, their initial

temperature at the time of the Creation can be estimated

19. On the philosophical question of whether there are other universes like ours in infinite space, the answer must be that until they impinge on our own universe and cause a disturbance in the observed furthermost matter, we have no means of knowing.

J.W. Salmon 1998

CHAPTER 2

The Dual Modes and Nature of the Human Mind

1. The human brain has evolved over thousands of years from that in the early primitive form of *homo erectus* (possibly comprising a large part of the cerebellum), to the present human form with its large overlaying cortex, comprising in most part the cerebrum. Both parts have access to the memory, which stores personalised images – as interpreted by the primitive brain – in response to its surroundings and local events: and stores data and real images as perceived by the developed cortex.

2. The primitive brain has been retained in modern man (and woman), and is similar to that in many animals. Its function is to induce emotional responses to new events and specific animal signals. These emotional responses act by releasing various, complex chemicals within the primitive brain to produce an appropriate physical response.

3. The chemicals released to the brain also produce

changes in the memory cells, so that similar future events and/or signals arouse emotional responses associated with the original events and signals. These emotions are therefore inherent in the process of learning, and form part of the instinctive behaviour for survival. Depending on the amount of the various chemicals released, the changes to the memory cells become more or less permanent.

4. The emotional responses may vary over a wide range; for example, mild interest may increase in intensity to become excitement or reduce in level of intensity to produce detachment. Similarly annoyance may increase to anger or reduce to become sanguine; and anxiety may increase to fear or reduce to a feeling of confidence and well being. These emotional ranges are associated with the level of chemicals produced in the primitive brain in response to signals received via the nervous system from the senses.

The nervous system also conveys signals to the glands and muscles to prepare the body for an appropriate movement or action. For example, when the primitive brain is angered the medulla parts of the adrenal glands are caused to release adrenalin into the blood supply to prepare an animal (or human), for attack or hostile behaviour. Conversely – in the case of fear – the activity of the primitive brain will cause adrenalin to be released to prepare the animal for flight. In extreme fear this brain ceases to control the glands or muscles. The cortex will note this effect and enter a state of shock, and there will be a traumatising of the memory cells. The cortex may then put a block on the recall of the circumstances that caused the shock, but the primitive brain will react with fear to similar circumstances. Careful therapy is required to help the cortex to release its block and to understand what caused the circumstances.

5. Part of the primitive brain remains alert at all times, even when most of it becomes inactive due to the sleep inducing chemicals. The senses of hearing, touch and smell can therefore continue to respond to any change in the immediate neighbourhood, thus allowing the animal (or human), to become fully aroused – including the cortex – and so respond to any threat or to a chance for food, etc.

During sleep the active part of the primitive brain continues to search the memory cells, which respond by recalling their most recent emotional excitations. Consequently images of experiences are sequentially recalled (like a replay), to produce the phenomenon of dreaming. The images, however, are dependent on the emotions which caused the associated impressions in the memory cells and are different for each individual; for example the emotions themselves vary with the current circumstances and past experiences of the individual.

The emotions – as indicated in section 4 – can vary over a wide range, although they are linked to only a few basic instinctive reactions (such as interest). The images produced in sleep are therefore dependent on the intensity of past and present emotional experiences and the impression that an individual has of an observation or experience during the fully wakened state. Consequently many dreams are of little concern, but occasionally may be stressful and even produce a "nightmare".

6. The formation of images is due to the ability of the memory cells to accurately store patterns perceived by the visual sense and its cognitive zones in both primitive and cortex parts of the brain. This facility enables the primitive brain to recognise present events and situations essential for survival; and for the cortex to recall the sequence of past

and present events as an aid to improving its fortunes. Images thus aid the process of memory and are often associated with emotions to recall events; they can also be used to form associations in the cortex, with data and other non-emotive subjects, to recall single and sequential items of information.

Images are not necessarily formed when remembering sounds, such as in music, since the latter are obviously stored sequentially: it is likely that a gradual sequence of emotions is important here to the process of memory. The activation of other senses too can be stored non-visually so that – for example – the subtle ingredients of a scent can be recreated by a complex mixture of chemicals, after perhaps years of trial and error, by retention of the original smell "in the mind".

7. The primitive brain relies upon its senses for its survival and its responses to these senses is extremely rapid. For example, sight is exceptionally fast in recognising changes to eye patterns and/or body stances/movements in other animals or human beings. In human beings the responses to the senses by the primitive part of the brain may not be understood by the cortex (whereas in animals the cortex is simpler and does not impede the response to signals from the senses).

Such responses, however, must produce an emotional reaction that affects the memory cells, which remind the human being or animal during sleep that an event occurred – during the day – of importance to its well being. The correct interpretation of dreams is therefore important for human beings, but this is only possible when the personalised images of the individual are understood. The interpretation is helped by the reviewing of dreams during the following morning and relating them to events during the past one or two days; but dire warnings in dreams may be related to threatening experiences from an earlier period.

8. Communication between primitive brains may also take place that will affect the memory cells and therefore complicate the dreams. This communication can be extremely rapid and is in the form of a sequence of images from one individual to another without either being immediately aware that the messages have been passed. They are therefore involuntary, i.e. not intended to be disclosed, but they often occur during an emotional moment when one individual is under stress. The consequent dreams of the recipient may then be of a disturbing or unusual nature.

Such messages can take place through eye contact, but may also occur through listening to another voice without either eye contact or conversation taking place. There is also the possibility of communication taking place between the minds of close relatives, during moments of stress of one of them, even though they may be separated by large distances.

This suggests that the memory cells can discharge their contents in the same sequence in which they were excited (similar to the replaying of long compositions of music "from memory"), via the nervous system to an unsuspecting individual through sight and sound, or by electromagnetic or some other form of wave as yet unknown.

9. The cortex evolved as an extension to the primitive brain as an aid to problem solving (which enabled the use of tools to be conceived), and to assess the beneficial (or otherwise), responses enacted by the primitive brain to its stimuli. This second function enabled early man and animals to live in groups and to recognise the benefit of

conforming to the leadership of an experienced and successful individual.

The human cortex has grown in complexity over that of other animals as it has gained in adaptability to provide for its biological needs, such as food, water, shelter, warmth and clothing, and procreation. It is recognised that – perhaps 10,000 years ago – this evolution enabled human groups to change from hunter/gatherers into farming communities.

The present level of complexity of the human brain appears to be capable of solving most – if not all – of the problems required of it by technology and in living in a global society, as well as recognising and coping with the urges exerted by the primitive part of the brain.

10. To permit this adaptability the cortex is divided into two lobes, whose functions are normally independent and grouped into zones or areas; so that – speech for example – is controlled by a zone on the left side of the cortex. There is little communication needed between the two lobes if the functions of the zones are performing well, but some duplication of activity takes place if one or more of the zones is damaged. There is also a possibility that the two lobes may compete for control of some of the instinctive reactions of the primitive brain; if – for example – there is doubt in the cortex about the integrity of the judicial, financial, religious and/or political institutions of society. This has the effect of reducing the emotional level of confidence – within the primitive brain – for these institutions. (Conversely the level of confidence may be falsely increased by the cortex acquiescing or submitting – using the choice of "free will" – to deceptively represented organisations, but with eventual disillusionment and recriminations.)

11. A phenomenon that occurs with some humans is for the cortex to be partly awake and be aware that it is asleep and dreaming. The cortex observes the progress of the dream with detachment and may attempt a verbal interruption of the sequence; but this is usually unsuccessful. The dream can be ended, however, by an attempt at actual physical movement.

12. The ability of the cortex to re-arrange its images of the real world in various patterns and to assess unusual circumstances allows discovery and invention to occur. This ability is available to anyone who pursues an aim with vision and determination.

13. The recognisable nature of individual humans and animals is called character; it is structured in the primitive brain (probably by the genes), and is as distinctive as fingerprints in humans and body markings in animals. It is moderated to some extent as the cortex learns how to adapt within a group or society, and will flourish or wither depending on the circumstances appertaining to the individual.

The character of an individual is retained within a group and is identified by traits that vary over ranges such as aggressive to submissive, generous to mean, extrovert to introvert, forthright to cunning, etc. The least admirable of these character traits is mollified, if the animal is in favourable circumstances, by the intervention of the cortex over the instinctive urges of the primitive brain.

14. The instinctive urges of the primitive part of the brain occur frequently; and the satisfying of these needs produces an aspect of behaviour called motivation. The need to provide food for the family, for example, motivates the male to earn a living in society; and when there is strong competition for scarce resources (e.g. jobs),

the motivation increases and may become ruthless. This has resulted in open conflict between groups and nations in the past. One of the problems to be adequately solved in the future is to ensure that there are sufficient natural resources available to meet the basic needs of all the world's populations.

15. Another motivation important to science and technology is curiosity. This probably arose from the instinctive urge to search for and assess new sources of food in early humans and animals. It could therefore have been the beginning of intelligence and the evolution of the cortex.

Motivations are therefore strongly reinforced and sustained by the bodily needs of the human and animal and require the exercising of the cortex to achieve their goals.

16. Desires are expressions of cravings for things other than those which support the basic needs for survival; as such they are associated with processes in the cortex, but give pleasurable emotions when gratified. They can be simply satisfied in a society whose basic needs are adequately supplied; or indulged in an affluent society that can supply much more than is required for survival.

An affluent society is sustained by exercising the cortex attributes of acumen, diligence, invention, imagination, learning and skills; but it engenders unattractive traits such as vanity, pride, acquisitiveness, envy, aggression and greed. However, it encourages some of the better aspects of human nature, such as generosity, amiability, honesty, dedication, inquisitiveness, compassion and courage.

CHAPTER 3

An Advocacy for the Existence of Electromagnetic and Gravity Ethers

3.1   Review

1. Our knowledge of electromagnetism is based on the research of M. Faraday, who discovered the law linking electricity with magnetism; and of J.C. Maxwell[i], who introduced the concept of unit charges and developed the theory of electromagnetic radiation.

2. An electromagnetic radiation in the visual spectrum is produced by an atom when one of its electrons "jumps" from one stable orbit to that of a lower energy orbit. The radiation releases energy which had previously been absorbed either from an incoming particle or from a pulse of external radiation. The two events follow each other rapidly, since the atom is unstable until it attains its normal, lowest energy "ground-state".

3. Gravitational theory was first propounded by Isaac Newton and later developed by Albert Einstein. Newton

was able to explain the motion of planets around the Sun by introducing the concepts of a gravitational force and the inertia possessed by a mass. Einstein realised that if the speed of light is constant – as discovered by the Michelson and Morley experiment – then the Newton values of mass and inertia, for matter that is approaching the speed of light, must change. Einstein used advanced mathematics in his study, which he called "The General Theory of Relativity", to obtain precise values for the changes in mass and inertia. His theory also showed that a beam of light will be bent in the gravitational field of a large mass, and every mass is an alternative fount of energy.

4. Neither Newton nor Einstein attempted to explain the nature of the attractive force which exists between all bodies of matter; Newton simply referred to the phenomenon as "action at a distance". Einstein deduced that the gravitational force is equivalent to the inertia force on a mass when the latter accelerates at the value g. Newton suspected that light consisted of small particles of energy, but proof of the existence of sub-atomic particles was not available to him. Particles that move at speeds approaching that of light were discovered during the early years of Einstein, who was then able to advance the work of Newton. Explanations are proposed in the Gravity Ether section for the source of the gravitational force and for inertia; and in the Propagation of Light section for the cause of the bending of light by gravity.

3.2   The Electromagnetic Ether Particles

5. Electromagnetic radiation extends over a wide spectrum of frequencies, but the earliest study of a narrow range of it was made by Isaac Newton with his research

into the nature of daylight. All electromagnetic radiation is now known to be two sinusoidally varying waves; one of magnetic flux, the other of electrical flux, whose maxima and minima are in time-phase, but whose planes of variation are 90 degrees apart in space. The direction of propagation through space is perpendicular to both the magnetic and the electric fluxes[i].

6. To achieve propagation through space requires a hypothesis regarding the nature of the medium through which the radiation travels. It is conjectured here that this medium, called the electromagnetic ether, requires four fundamental particles, which fill all space throughout the universe and which can permeate the interstices of matter.

7. For an explanation of the two particles associated with the electrical flux the concept of J.C. Maxwell is used. Suppose two isolated metal spheres are spaced some distance apart in a vacuum and an electrical potential difference (p.d.) is applied to the spheres. If the p.d. is changing a current will flow through the vacuum; this current was attributed by Maxwell to the flow of unit electrical charges (which are now known to be of negative potential), towards the positive sphere.

8. The force acting on each unit charge was assumed to be due to an electrical "field", which was represented by "lines of force" bridging the gap between the spheres. However, it could be construed that these lines of force follow the distribution of a second type of fundamental particle, here denoted as a potential energy particle,(or pep). A pep is normally stationary in space and is electrically neutral, but becomes charged, with positive and negative charges at either end, in the vicinity of a p.d. Such particles can form long chains and exert attraction forces on the unit charges and on the two spheres forming

the field. These peps must then be in tension, but they must also be capable of being in compression to produce repulsion forces between like charges.

9. If the p.d. between the spheres approaches a steady state the movement of unit charges continues until the p.d. between the spheres is equal and opposite to that of the source (e.g. a battery). The electrical current flow then ceases and the unit charges remain stationary in the field of the peps. Energy is stored in the pep field with the unit charges and this energy is returned to the source when the p.d. is reduced or interrupted. (Some of the source energy is lost due to a pulse of radiation from the gap while the current is increasing or decreasing).

10. Suppose now that the electrical circuit connected to the spheres has an adjacent, straight section of conductor also enclosed within the vacuum. When the current is flowing the electrical field continues within the conductor, although this field will be of much lower intensity than that required across the spheres gap for the same current flow. The unit charges excite the atoms when they enter the positive sphere and electrons then form the current flow within the conductor.

11. If the current is increasing the electrical field within the conductor is reduced by an opposing pep field, which reduces the quantity/velocity of the flowing electrons (as discovered by M. Faraday). This phenomenon was attributed to a magnetic field, which surrounds the current. This field was first discovered by H.C. Oersted, who observed that a compass needle was deflected by a current flowing in an adjacent wire; it was therefore thought to be magnetic in nature. The magnetic lines of force are – by analogy with the electric field – considered here to be formed by fundamental magnetic energy

particles,(meps). They are normally neutral and stationary in space but can become polarised in the vicinity of an electrical current, with a north and south pole at either end. The analogy also requires a fourth particle (possibly the unit pole that P.A.M. Dirac predicted[ii]), to form the magnetic flux and to transport magnetic energy in a specific direction when the field is changing. The polarity of the unit pole is here taken to be south, so that the unit pole flows from a south to a north polarity in a mep field. If the current reaches a steady state the unit poles become stationary in the mep field and energy is stored within the field. If the current is reduced the collapsing magnetic field will generate a pep field, which tends to maintain the current flow, and energy is thereby returned to the source. (While the current is changing an electromagnetic (e.m.) wave radiates some energy from the conductor in all directions, generated by the electric and magnetic fields within the conductor).

When a steady current flows in a closed loop (including that produced by the orbital electrons in iron crystals), the loop becomes polarised by the meps, which can exert a force on other current loops. The direction of the force is in the direction of potential energy flow, i.e. perpendicular to the direction of both the meps field and the remote current. Depending on the direction of the force the meps are either in tension or compression and there is attraction or repulsion between the loops respectively.

12. Conclusions. All the fundamental ether particles are too small to be detectable at present, but are considered to have zero mass; are normally stationary and neutral in space; and the peps and meps can be polarised in the presence of source p.d.s and electron currents respectively. They are all capable of permeating the interstices of

elementary particle matter, such as that between protons and electrons. Energy can be stored or transmitted in a pep field by the unit charges and in a mep field by the unit poles. The peps and the meps have rigid forms that can transmit tension and compression forces through their chains at a speed greater than that of light; (as suggested by the EPR experiment, described below).

3.3 The Propagation of Light through the Electromagnetic Ether

13. When an electron moves from one orbit to another – of smaller orbit and lower energy – it first leaves the higher orbit at a narrow angle and then curves inwards towards the nucleus; but due to its relativistic inertia it continues in orbit around the nucleus. The shape of its orbit – with successive passes around the nucleus – is approximately elliptical of large eccentricity. The resulting rotating field (of peps), between the electron and the nucleus, pulls unit charges towards the nucleus, where they form a negative layer that reduces the strength of the electric field. The successive passes of the electron also produces a cloud of unit poles, which maintain their positions after the electron has passed, and subsequently react with the electron to reduce the velocity of the latter. The orbit therefore broadens and eventually becomes stable and circular, where it neither gains nor loses energy, with the electric and magnetic (combined with the gravitational) forces on the electron in balance.

14. The plane of the orbit does not change while the electron is in its transient locus; hence the plane of the electric field – and the direction in space of the magnetic field inside the orbit – do not change. The strengths of the

fields vary from a maximum at the perigee to a minimum at the apogee. The electric field is limited to virtually a line between the electron and the nucleus, while the magnetic field is contained within a thin disc perpendicular to the electron's trajectory. Consequently the fields are spaced 90 degrees apart only at the perigee and apogee, but their components – in the two directions parallel to the minor axis of the ellipse – vary sinusoidally about a mean level. The variations gradually diminish to zero and the mean level diminishes to a constant value when the orbit stabilises. The variations in amplitude of the electric and magnetic fields cause the unit charges and unit poles surrounding the orbit to respond sinusoidally, thereby producing two e.m. waves 180 degrees apart, co-linear with – and in the same plane – as the minor axis of the ellipse. (The mean levels of the two fields do not contribute to the e.m. waves.)

15. The frequency of the generated e.m. wave is constant and is determined by the velocity of the electron around the changing elliptical orbit; and the velocity of the wave is limited by the speed of transmission of energy through the ether by the unit charges and the unit poles (i.e. the speed of light). The speed of transmission cannot vary, even if the star – which produces the radiation – is moving at great speed. The result is a change in the frequency of the e.m. wave, due to the Doppler effect.

16. In the relatively cool gas of the atmosphere that surrounds a star the atoms are not jostled as rapidly as those in the very hot plasma of the gas inside the star. If a single quantum of the radiation emitted by the star is from an excited atom of a particular chemical element, it will be absorbed by an atom of the same element in the star's atmosphere. Although the absorbed energy makes the

atom unstable there may follow a considerable period before the atom emits a photon – from a recovering electron – in a radial direction towards the Earth. (Radiations in other directions are dispersed into space). The spectrum of the star will therefore have gaps (known as Fraunhofer dark lines), in its spectrum of radiation from all of its chemical elements. The dark lines give proof of the chemical composition of a star.

The dark lines appear in the spectrum where the star's radiation bright lines should be, and they are shifted towards either the red or blue end of a rest-state spectrum (at the Earth), depending on the velocity of the star and its atmosphere with respect to the Earth. Although there will be an occasional photon emitted towards the Earth, the colour of the dark lines appears to be completely black.

17. The recessional velocities of the galaxies and stars were discovered by E.P. Hubble. Each star's recessional velocity is determined by its red shift when viewed from the Earth. The velocity is given by the formula:

$$v = c \frac{(1 - k)}{(1 + k)}$$

where c is the velocity of light
and k is observed frequency/(original frequency)^2.[iii]

Hubble also discovered that most stars and galaxies are receding from the Earth and their recessional velocities are proportional to their distance from the Earth. The distances could be determined geometrically for stars that are not too remote: for greater distances Hubble used various astronomical assessment methods, such as the known luminosity of a particular type of star compared with its reduced luminosity when measured at the Earth.

Hubble knew that the velocity of light is constant everywhere in the universe, based on the Michelson-Morley experiment and Einstein's subsequent assumption. It had also been discovered that the red shift was due to the whole spectrum of a star being reduced in frequency. The calculated distances, however, assumed that the Earth has zero velocity in any direction; moreover it is clear that the calculations required that the ether must have zero velocity everywhere in the universe; and that light travels in straight lines radially towards the Earth in a spherical universe filled with galaxies and stars.

Michelson and Morley were fortunate in attempting to measure the velocity of light through an ether on a planet that has virtually zero velocity in space. Their belief was that the ether – if it existed – flowed with an independent velocity past the Earth and would affect the velocity of light. Their results showed that the velocity of light – measured in any direction – did not change. They concluded that the ether did not exist; they dismissed the possibility that its velocity in space was also zero.

The experiment, however, was important for both Einstein and Hubble, who profited from the knowledge that the velocity of light is constant in every direction. Einstein assumed that it was constant everywhere in the universe, and used this as the basis for his Special Theory of Relativity. Hubble used it as the basis for his measurements of distances to stars and galaxies.

18. Each photon of light that reaches the Earth retains the frequency – with its red or blue shift – with which it was emitted from a star. Due to the persistence of vision of the human eye the colours become mixed and – for the Sun – they produce white light. Newton revealed the range of colour frequencies of sunlight by passing the light,

via a pin hole, through a prism to produce its spectrum. Subsequent tests by Newton showed that the separate colours did not change if their light was passed through another prism.

The speed of light through a glass prism is reduced by different amounts depending on the frequency of the photon. The speed of violet light is slower than that of red light because the higher frequency of the former causes its photons to undergo a greater number of deflections – per unit length – by the atoms of the glass. When the light emerges from the prism there is a small dispersion of the beam of each colour, due to the deflections that occur at the exit surface of the prism. The beams merge in the spectrum to produce colour mixing at the boundaries between the true frequencies.

19. For white light (e.g. from an incandescent lamp), that is collimated and passed through a diffraction grating, there are photons of the light that pass with very little deflection through the gaps to produce a white image on a screen behind the grating. For those photons that undergo greater deflections, due to their encounters with the atoms at the exit corners of the gaps, the red colour photons receive the greatest deflections. This is due to their lower frequency and therefore lower energy; and hence the greater effect of the attractive fields of the grating atoms on their trajectories. The result is two spectrums on either side of the central white image with the red colours furthest from the centre.

20. When light that is not collimated is directed at two slits that are a short distance apart, the emerging beams mix their colour photons to produce interference patterns on a screen placed behind the slits. This interference occurs when the photons of a given frequency have both their

electric and magnetic fields passing through zero (since their peaks are in phase); or other colour photons of a nearby frequency have their fields in phase opposition to those of the given frequency. The image on the screen is then a band of white and dark stripes.

21. The phenomenon of the bending of a light beam when it passes close to a star is well known and can produce the effect called "gravitational lensing"[(iii)]. Most descriptions of the effect attribute the bending of the beam to the photons acquiring mass when propagated through space; (their rest mass being accepted as zero). This is said to explain their attraction towards the star by its gravitational field. However there may be an alternative explanation for "gravitational lensing", if the mass of the photons is to remain at zero, since the bending is simply an effect on a wave of e.m. radiation propagated through the ether particles.

An alternative explanation assumes that the mass of all photons is zero, but that the e.m. wave of any photon is influenced by the unit mass field of the gravity ether. This implies the possibility that energy can flow from an e.m. ether to a gravity ether. From the observed effect it is known that the photon loses some of its energy, resulting in an increase of its red shift. It is concluded, therefore, that the flow of energy is towards the star and that the photon beam will be deflected in that direction. The total deflection will be the same as that predicted by Einstein, but the explanation here avoids the difficult mathematics and is easier to visualise. It also avoids the esoteric explanation of space-time warping around a star.

22. The EPR experiment, proposed by A. Einstein, B. Podolsky and N. Rosen, was designed to check the Quantum Theory prediction that e.m. effects, emanating

from the same source, can be transmitted across space at a speed faster than light. The original proposal envisaged using electrons but later it was decided to use photons. These would be a pair that were produced simultaneously by a single atom (and would inherently be transmitted 180 degrees apart in space); and would traverse polarising filters to set their polarisations 180 degrees apart. The purpose of the polarisation difference was to ensure their propagating magnetic fields were in phase opposition (in space), and would therefore cancel out and not affect the result of the experiment. The experiment was performed by A. Aspect and his colleagues of the University of Paris.

The photons travelled in opposite directions down a long tube, at one end of which one photon was deflected so that its polarisation was changed. Accurate timing and sensing confirmed that the polarisation of the other photon changed at the same instant, before any light signal had time to travel the length of the tube. This seemed to deny Einstein's prediction that no transmission of energy could travel at a speed faster than light.

However, a possible explanation for the anomaly is the latent magnetic field of the atom, which generated the two photons. The photons are produced in the ether by the variations in the magnetic field of the atom about a mean value, which decays to a stable level when the atom returns to its ground state. The meps of this main field would therefore be contiguous with the unit poles of the photons; and it is a property of the meps that enables them to transmit signals through their chains at a speed faster than light.

The EPR experiment in essence confirmed that the e.m. wave of one photon transmits a change, to the directions of its unit south poles, back to the source field;

which immediately transmits the variation to the second photon.

23. On the philosophical question, "what is energy?", it is possible to describe its effect on the fundamental particles and matter, but its source is conjectured to be the base medium from which the e.m. and gravity ethers evolved, following the process of Creation. As a result the base medium has been depleted (slightly) of some of its energy, which is consequently stored in the universe ethers.

References

(i) *The Electromagnetic Field.* G.W. Carter, Longmans.

(ii) *Directions in Physics.* P.A.M. Dirac, Wiley.

(iii) *Essentials of Astronomy.* L. Motz and A. Duveen, Columbia Univ. Press.

Further reading

The Stuff of the Universe. J. Gribbin and M. Rees, Penguin.

Quantum Reality: Beyond the New Physics. N. Herbert, Rider.

God's Equation. A. Aczel, Judy Perkins.

The Magic Furnace. M. Chown, Vintage.

Cosmic Bullets. R. Clay and B. Dawson, Allen and Unwin.

3.4   The Gravity Ether and its Particles

24. By analogy with the electric and magnetic fields the gravitational field is assumed to consist of two fundamental particles. One is a gravitational potential energy particle (gep), that can attach itself either to other geps to form long chains; or to the electrically neutral particles of mass. The geps have a semi-rigid structure that allows the

transmission of tension waves on matter through their chains, but precludes the application of compression waves. Tension waves are transmitted at a speed that is faster than that of light.

The second particle, the unit mass particle, is the building block of all matter. They combine with geps as the source of energy in elementary particles (such as protons and electrons), and may have the form either of vibrating strings (as suggested by the Super String Theory), or – possibly – of vibrating spheres. They are normally stationary in space and fill the whole of the universe, but act independently from the geps to produce a force on elementary particle matter when its mass is either accelerating or decelerating. The force is ascribed to the inertia of the mass.

Both particles are electrically and magnetically neutral and can permeate the interstices of elementary particles of matter; but the geps have zero mass whereas the unit mass particle has an infinitesimally small but finite mass.

25. The geps exert a force of attraction between all elementary particles. The force is minute until an agglomeration of the elementary particles reaches the size of a planet or a star. Newton defined the force of attraction between two such masses as:

$$\text{force } f_g = G \times \frac{\text{product of two masses}}{d^2}$$

where G is Newton's Universal Gravitational Constant, and d is the distance between their centres of gravity.

If a small mass, travelling with high velocity, enters the gravitational field of a very large mass, it will be acted upon by three forces; (i) the gep force, (ii) the reaction (i.e. inertia) force, which opposes the gep force, viz.:

$$f_i = \text{relativity mass} \times \text{acceleration};$$

and (iii) the inertia force due to any change in its linear velocity. The resulting trajectory will be either unstable (i.e. the locus of a parabola, hyperbola or a collision course) or stable (viz. the orbit of a circle or an ellipse). A circular orbit is extremely rare, since a small disruptive force will push the small mass into an elliptical orbit.

If the orbit is an ellipse the vectorial difference, between the gep force and the inertia forces, causes the small mass to gain energy (and mass) over part of the ellipse and lose it over the other part of the orbit (which includes the apogee). For the orbit to be stable the gep force must act instantaneously (i.e. at a speed faster than light), between the two masses. In contrast the inertia forces act directly, and therefore instantaneously, on the smaller mass in its orbit.

26. Elementary particle matter gains mass (and energy) when the particle velocity is increased, including the effect of a deflection from its forward direction, since either circumstance produces an acceleration. (Conversely a particle loses mass when it decelerates). Newton deduced the law that determines the force required to produce an acceleration, which has been defined as the inertia force.

If the accelerating force applied to a mass is sustained the latter will gain kinetic energy as well as mass energy as more of the unit mass particles become absorbed into the mass. The velocity of the mass will continue to increase until the velocity of light is attained, whereupon the mass would become infinitely large. This suggests that there is a physical law linking the rate of energy transfer from the e.m. ether to the gravity ether. In particular there is the possibility of energy transfer from an e.m. wave to a large body as the wave passes close by the latter. The conditions at the velocity of light imply that they are at the boundary of the physical laws controlling the universe.

Newton regarded the force to accelerate a body as due to the inherent inertia of its mass, without giving the cause of the inertia. However, it is a convenient concept, which allows the combined effects of the gravity particles to be simply expressed mathematically. Indeed the laws of classical dynamics are founded on Newton's formulae.

27. Since it became known that large masses and sub-atomic particles could approach the speed of light it was necessary to adapt the classical theory of dynamics, which Einstein achieved with his Special and General Theories of Relativity. However, it was soon realised that e.m. radiation did not obey the laws of either Newton or Einstein; radiation theory required the mathematics of e.m. quanta. A successful theory called Quantum Electrodynamics (QED) was developed, but this involved the mathematics of probability with wave theory, so that some of its predictions were difficult to relate to physical reality. For example it concluded that e.m. quanta events in the universe could occur simultaneously (a fact that Einstein could not accept, since it meant exceeding the speed of light), but the EPR experiment appeared to confirm the conclusion. This exposition suggests that ether particles may be involved in this phenomenon, but until the present day the existence of e.m. and gravity ethers has been ignored.

28. The laws governing sub-atomic particles and nuclear physics have been explored with the theory called

Quantum Chromodynamics (QCD), which evolved from QED, but this still has some problems to overcome. Meanwhile a Grand Unified Theory (GUT), to which Einstein devoted his later years, is being sought. The aim of this theory is to combine Einstein's gravitational (i.e. relativity) theory with both QED and QCD. This is the goal of twenty-first century physicists, who are well aware of the possibility of fundamental particles with the extensive work being done on string theory.

CHAPTER 4

Speculations on Energy and Matter

4.1 Preamble

1. The ancient Greek philosopher, Democritus, reasoned that all matter was structured from indivisible particles, which he called atoms. Today we know that atoms are not indivisible, but are composed of protons, neutrons and electrons. Moreover, latest research has revealed that protons are composed of three quarks; while electrons are part of an elementary group of particles called leptons.

2. Many other particles – composed of three quarks – have also been discovered and they form a group referred to as hadrons. Another group, composed of two quarks (one quark and one anti-quark), comprises mesons.

3. The search for the ultimate indivisible particles, called the fundamental particles, seems near to realisation. It is believed that such particles came into being during the process of Creation, and that they cannot be altered by any natural or artificially contrived event. These particles may turn out to be the unit mass, the unit of electrical charge and the unit magnetic pole.

4. The next higher forms of matter, which have evolved from the fundamental particles, are called the elementary particles, such as electrons and quarks. Elementary particles possess the observed properties of mass and electrical charge (+/- and 0), and – when acted upon by natural forces – these particles form themselves into hadrons, mesons and leptons.

5. Of themselves the fundamental and elementary particles have no guiding forces, which determine how physical events will proceed. The first of these forces was discovered by Isaac Newton during his study on the motion of planets around the Sun. This led Newton to suggest that the universe was a vast mechanism of interdependent astronomical bodies under the control of a single gravitational force, from which all of their motions could be determined.

6. The study of electric charges and magnets in the 19th century showed that there must be electric and magnetic forces that are similar in form to that of the gravitational force: and J.C. Maxwell developed the studies of M. Faraday to propose an electromagnetic theory for varying electric and magnetic fields.

7. Nuclear physics had progressed in the 20th century to the point where two further forces were needed to be defined to describe the behaviour of elementary particles. These forces have been called the strong and the weak respectively, to explain the phenomena of nuclear stability and the apparently random, gradual disintegration of atoms due to radio–activity.

4.2 The Relationship between Force and Energy

8. Considering the gravitational field; a small mass, m,

in the field is acted upon by the gravitational force, which produces the acceleration of m. The field consequently increases the potential energy of m and its kinetic energy. An expression for the potential energy, at any point in the field, is assumed to involve massless potential energy particles (PEPs) (that form the gravity-ether's lines of force in the field); and unit mass particles, which are attracted along the lines of force whenever there is a change in the source potential-difference. The source potential-difference is due to a large mass, M (acting above a remote zero potential); and the total potential energy in the field is directly proportional to M, as derived from Einstein's formula $E = M.c^2$. The field strength S, at any point in the field is the density of the PEPs at that point; and the attraction force on m is $F = S.m$. The change of potential energy of mass m is $F \times$ distance through which m has been propelled along the lines of force; and the change in its kinetic energy is $^1/_2.m.v^2$, assuming that m started with velocity $v = 0$.

9. If the motions of the planets are in circular orbits around a star, they are kept in equilibrium by two forces; viz. the gravitational force which pulls the planets towards the star; and the centrifugal reaction or inertia force, which forces the planets away from the star, due to their inward radial accelerations in the star's gravitational field. If their orbits are ellipses there is a resultant third force, which causes the planets to increase and decrease their speeds in their trajectories around each ellipse.

10. The nature of the gravitational force and the stability of potential energy values indicates that both are normally unvarying. However, violent disturbances in some astronomical bodies cause longitudinal potential energy waves to radiate energy away from the source

(through the unit mass ether), and thereby produce a redistribution of the PE field. Such waves involve the movement of mass as well as energy; they therefore have only a relatively short range through space and exist for only a relatively short period.

4.3   The Structure of Elementary Particles

4.3.1   Hadrons and mesons

11. With the assumption that the unit electric charge particle has 1/3rd the charge of the electron, the u quark must contain two unit charge particles (scalar addition), either positive or negative; and the d quark has one unit charge particle, either positive or negative

12. Since an elementary particle, such as the proton, which has a mass equivalent of 938.3MeV – while its u,u and d quarks have masses of only 5MeV and 10MeV respectively – it must have the greater part of its mass in a central, or core, agglomeration of unit mass particles. Similarly every elementary particle comprises a central or core mass with its quarks in 1, 2 or 3 orbits.

13. The following simple representations assume that all the quark orbits are circular, however – if their orbits are elliptical – their mathematical or geometric constructions will be more complex.

14. The configuration of a particle, such as the Δ^{++}, which contains three positive u quarks, is therefore conjectured to have a central mass with its three u quarks displaced by 120 degrees in the same circular orbit around the central mass. These quarks are conveniently referred to as R, G and B quarks and – because each has a positive electric charge of 2 units – they repel each other with an

equal force. The nett electric force on each quark is therefore radially outwards.

15. A centrifugal force also acts on each of these R, G and B quarks, which is determined by the mass of the quark and its speed in orbit, but the nett force — (vector addition) — on the central mass is zero.

16. A further force acts on the quarks, viz. the strong force, which is assumed to be the gravitational force between the central mass and each of the R, G and B quarks. The nett pull on the central mass is zero, and the three forces acting on each quark must also sum to zero, to keep the quarks in a precise circular orbit.

17. Every hadron has a structure consisting of three quarks, but the latter may be in different orbits and displaced by different angles depending on the mass, the electric charge and the speed in orbit of each quark. For example the proton is conjectured as having its two u quarks at either end of a chord, which passes tangentially through the d quark gyrating in a smaller orbit.

18. The neutron's d,d,u quarks are similarly assumed to lie on a diametrical chord, with a d quark at each end and the u quark attached to the central mass.

19. The configuration of mesons is simpler in that they comprise only two quarks, which are of the same mass but are of opposite electric polarity and are conjectured to be displaced by 180 degrees around a single orbit. The electromagnetic force of attraction between the quarks is small compared with the strong force, but the former force produces the previously assumed annihilation of the quarks and the consequent short lifetimes of the mesons if the latter are in dynamic instability following a disturbance.

4.3.2 Leptons

20. The electron has a negative electric charge of 1 electron standard unit (esu), and therefore it is conjectured to comprise 3 negative unit charge particles. These are assumed to be in the same orbit around a central mass and – because unit charge particles have no mass – the latter must be attached to 3 small mass particles (possibly unit mass particles), to provide stability. This arrangement is very stable because the forces acting on the three particles are symmetrical. However the electron's dynamic system can be disrupted either by particle bombardment or by radiation.

21. The positron is similar to the electron except that it has a positive electric charge of +1 esu. The muon and tau have either positive or negative electric charges of 1 esu, but have central masses much greater than that of the electron.

22. The neutrinos associated with the electron, positron, muon and tau have no electric charge, but they are considered by the QED theory to have spin momentum. However it seems unlikely that they have any orbiting particles, since the latter would have no stabilising forces acting on their circumferential position. Their masses are small compared with their associated leptons – and in the case of the electron's neutrino, its mass may compare closely with that of a single unit mass.

4.4   The Strong Force

23. At the core of every elementary particle is its central mass, which may comprise a large number of unit mass particles; and around the core there are 2 or 3 quarks in orbit, but these are mainly associated with the stability and the electric charge of the particle.

24. The strong force has its source in the central mass, which is an extremely dense concentration of matter, since the unit masses in the core are pulled closely together by their gravitational field. The total gravitational field in – and surrounding – the core stores the energy attributed to the latter, as expressed by Einstein's formula, $E = m.c^2$.

25. Due to the small value of the mass m the extent of the energy field is limited to approximately atomic dimensions, hence the field strength is effectively high over that short range. If the assumptions are made (i) that the gravitational field strength at the surface of the central core has the same value as the field strength at the surface of the Sun, and (ii) the Universal Gravitation Constant applies for the sub-atomic field, then the diameter of the central mass, m, is extremely small compared with the diameters of the quark orbits.

26. Research has revealed that the strong force appears to reverse and become a repulsion force as the surface of the central mass is approached. It is therefore surmised that an approaching elementary particle produces a preceding shock wave, which is a longitudinal wave in the unit mass ether that is similar to a soliton wave in water. The shock wave transmits energy between the incoming particle and the central mass m – with probable reflections off the latter – the effect being to apply a reverse force on the particle and a reaction movement forwards of the central mass. The shock wave and its reflections have been detected and have been interpreted as a zero-charge, massless particle called a gluon, which also plays a part in the resonance stability of a proton – and other particles – and the nucleus of an atom.

27. A sustained acceleration of the central mass in space is dependent on the external gravitational field of a large

mass M (e.g. the Sun), which is superimposed on the strong force field of m. As its speed in space increases the mass of m will increase due to the accretion of unit mass particles onto the central mass; the latter therefore only gains mass when it is accelerated by an external field.

4.5   Binding Energy at the Atomic Level

28. The energy in the field surrounding an isolated central mass is greater than when the latter forms part of a group of atoms in a chemical element[i]. This is because the lines of force, from the central masses of the other atoms, pull and distort the radial force lines from the previously isolated central mass. Consequently the density of the core and the lines of force from the latter are reduced and the energy in its field is diminished proportionately. The difference in energy between the two fields – i.e. for the isolated mass and for the mass surrounded by a group of atoms – is called the binding energy (B.E.); which is therefore a measure of the change in mass.

29. The electric charge of an isolated chemical ion is that which is detected by a mass spectrograph, which determines its associated mass; (the mass of the orbiting electrons of the excited atom is neglected).[iv] In the case of a hydrogen ion, the increase in mass over the expected value for 1/16th of the oxygen ion (the standard for atomic mass) is significant and is the source of the energy that fuels the atomic fusion at the birth and early evolution of stars.

4.6 The Natural Decay of Chemical Elements

30. Most chemical elements decay into stable forms over varying periods of time, some of which may extend

over millions of years. Examples of these are given in reference (i) and their gradual decay, which may progress through numerous steps – and involve a different element at each step – follows a strictly repetitive sequence. Thus for the decay of U238 the first few steps always produce the same sequence, Th234, Pa234, U234, and ends with the stable element Pb206 after a 10 step sequence. At the various steps a chemical may become a naturally occurring isotope, either proton rich or neutron rich, in a process called radio-activity.

31. During the decay there may be branching, i.e. two or more different elements emerge from a single element, thereby forming either a eutectic alloy, or lighter fluids or gases; alternatively the sequence may revert to a single element from the alloy. Nevertheless the inevitability of each step is due to the dynamic control of the nuclei and their orbiting electrons.

32. The decay of elements therefore suggests that the orbital electrons of the atoms are controlled accurately within very close limits of energy, angular position and speed, spin and orbital parameters; very much like the planets of the solar system as they perform predictable gyrations around the Sun. Over different periods of time the electrons – of a given atom – reach critical conjunctions with respect to each other, thereby causing the atom to become conditionally stable and susceptible to low energy radiations or neutrinos; a release of energy then takes place to enable the atom to reach a more stable, lower energy state.

33. The conjunction of two or three electrons enables at least one critical electron to become shielded from the electromagnetic attraction of the nucleus and there will be an interaction with one of the few cosmic gamma rays or

particles (e.g. electron-neutrinos) that penetrate the atom. The weak radial pull on the electron allows it to escape from the atom, which achieves another step in its decay. The release of energy thus achieved may be with the ejected electron, which is known as a beta particle, and is part of the radio-activity. (The beta particle has a wide range of escape velocities, affected by the direction of travel of the electron in one of its various orbits when it reacts with the cosmic ray / particle).

34. Two other forms of energy release are also possible, viz. an alpha particle and a gamma ray; the former occurs when a nucleus interacts with a high energy cosmic ray and ejects a group of two protons and two neutrons (a helium nucleus), as a single particle. (An alpha particle has two escape velocities, suggesting that it is affected by the spin of the nucleus). A gamma ray photon is due to a high energy electron (which has received prior energy from a cosmic ray interaction), descending to a lower energy orbit. The release of energy achieved with an alpha, beta or gamma ray ejection is also part of the process called radio-activity; and the force necessary to produce the activity is known as the weak force.

35. The radio-activity is continuous for each unstable element and follows an exponential curve with time for the intensity of the activity[i]. The radiation is randomly emitted because the millions of atoms – of the given element in a large mass – do not have their electron orbits in synchronism, nor are their nuclear vibrational movements in unison. However, for what appears to be a random emission, there is the underlying orderliness of electron orbital gyrations and the identifying features of an exponential decay curve and a well defined half-life time for every chemical element.

4.7 The Weak Force

36. The phenomenon of radio-activity was discovered by H. Becquerel in 1896, when he discovered the effect of uranium salts – left unattended above an object – on an unexposed photographic plate. Subsequent research on the phenomenon, by Marie and Pierre Curie in 1898, proved that radio-activity was either an emission of electromagnetic waves or particles. This was confirmed by E. Rutherford's independent research in 1898, and he named the two emissions that he recorded as alpha and beta rays. Rutherford also went on to discover a third kind of emission, which he called gamma rays.

37. The energy levels involved in the radio-activity research at that period were very low, of the order 0.01 keV to 10 MeV, which could be produced by alpha, beta or gamma rays from radio-active metals. It was therefore assumed that the activity was due to a previously unknown weak force, unrelated to the electromagnetic or gravitational forces.

38. Later it was realised that the newly discovered cosmic rays were also a cause of radio-activity in heavy elements, and the attention of astronomers was drawn into this pioneering research. Extensive research on cosmic rays showed that they have an enormous range of energies, i.e. from 100MeV to 100Tera MeV, and were easily capable of disintegrating the nuclei of atoms. Fortunately these natural disintegrations only occur to atoms in the upper atmosphere, from which only the relatively low-energy and relatively stable particles (viz. muons, electrons and neutrinos) reach the Earth's surface.

39. A theory that had been developed (initially by Enrico Fermi circa 1935) to explain radio-activity as due to a weak force, had therefore to be extended to

encompass the bombardment of chemical elements by cosmic ray particles. This came to be known as the electro-weak theory, but unfortunately the misnomer of the weak force has persisted.

4.8 The Transmutation and Fission of Atoms by Bombardment

40. Various particles have been used as projectiles for bombardment, e.g. electrons, protons, neutrons, deuterons, alpha and beta particles and gamma rays. The first transmutation was obtained by E. Rutherford (1919)[iv], on nitrogen gas – using a beam of alpha particles from a radioactive source – to produce oxygen gas and a release of protons.

41. The initial impact causes an alpha particle (a helium nucleus) to momentarily bond with a nitrogen nucleus to form a compound nucleus of fluorine, containing all nine orbiting electrons. A compound nucleus is usually unstable and in this case it ejects a proton, leaving oxygen as the product nucleus. However, a summation of the equivalent-mass energies, before the impact and after the oxygen formation (based on a nuclear reaction equation), shows that the final energy is slightly greater than the initial energy. The combined energies of the oxygen nucleus and isolated proton are therefore slightly greater than those of the nitrogen nucleus and isolated alpha particle. This result confirms that part of the kinetic energies of the system have been absorbed by the nett potential energy field, thus increasing the combined mass.

42. The completed nuclear reaction equation includes an assessment of the change in mass to the alpha particle due to its acceleration in the Sun's gravitational field; and

the change to the binding energy of the alpha particle as it merges into the compound nucleus. Throughout the energy changes the unit mass particles, which effect the changes, remain unaltered; they are therefore regarded as fundamental particles.

43. Fission of heavy nuclei can be obtained by increasing the energy of the projectile particle; but J.D. Cockcroft and E. Walton showed that it is also possible to split the nuclei of light atoms with lower energy particles (1932). They obtained their result by bombarding lithium with protons using an accelerating voltage of 800kV.[iii] As in the previous case the initial impact forms a compound nucleus; however, the latter cannot achieve stability by ejecting a single particle from its nucleus, but instead ejects a number of neutrons and/or protons from the nucleus. The resulting fissure may split the nucleus in almost equal parts or in several fragments; in most cases this results in the release of binding energy from the potential energy (i.e. equivalent mass energy) field to the kinetic energy of the fragments and ejected elementary particles.

4.9   Collisions between Particles

44. Particle collisions are a frequent natural occurrence in the atmosphere, involving high energies and the disintegration of atoms and/or particles. However, natural laws – affecting forces and matter – control the outcome of each collision to conserve energy, electric charge, linear and orbital spin, quark and lepton structures; and the subsequent trajectories of matter.

45. Experiments to reproduce specific particle collisions require very large particle-accelerators (e.g. proton, anti-proton colliders), which increase the closing-velocities

between particles to very nearly the speed of light.[ii] At these velocities the protons have their relativistic masses increased to approximately 40 times their rest mass. After a delay − required to achieve the high velocities − the protons and anti-protons (which are rotating in opposite directions around the collider) are steered into head-on collisions in a detector. The resulting movements of the fragments (as revealed in bubble and streamer chambers), enable the behaviour of particles at sub-atomic levels to be studied.

46. The initial result of a proton/anti-proton collision is for the central masses of the protons (+&−), to partially or totally merge and form the core of a heavy particle, viz. either a $W^{+/-}$ (with a mass equivalent of 83GeV), or a neutral Z^0 (with a mass equivalent of 93GeV). These energies are momentarily conserved from that finally attained in the collider, suggesting that the accrued unit mass particles − on the rest masses of the protons − take a finite time to disperse.

47. When the relativistic conditions no longer apply, i.e. immediately after the collision, the merged heavy particle, i.e. W or Z, ejects unit mass particles to reach the next lower level of energy, which − in the case of a W^+ particle − may be a top and an anti-bottom quark. These quarks are ejected in opposite directions at different velocities to conserve momentum and both decay rapidly to achieve the next lower level of energy.[v] The time taken between the collision and ejection of the quarks is extremely short; such that the movement of the W particle produces no discernible displacement trace in a bubble chamber.

48. The structure of the W particle is thought to be similar to that of a proton, but with u, u and d quarks

orbiting around a larger central mass equivalent of approximately 83GeV; while the Z particle is probably similar in form to a neutron, except that the former has a central mass equivalent of approximately 93GeV.

49. The structures of the top and bottom quarks must consequently be part of the contents released by either the W or the Z particle. The top quark – released by a W^+ particle – is therefore conjectured to have a central mass equivalent of approximately 40GeV with u, u, and d quarks orbiting around the central mass; while the bottom quark also has u, u and d quarks with a central mass equivalent of approximately 5GeV.

50. Further decays then follow as the top and bottom quarks eject more particles to disperse the remainder of the energy from the proton and anti-proton collision. The top quark simultaneously ejects a bottom quark (which subsequently ejects a jet of hadrons) with an electron and an anti-neutrino; while the previous bottom quark ejects a separate jet of hadrons. (The hadrons are fragments of matter, which rapidly capture appropriate quarks from the gravity and electromagnetic ethers to form viable particles.)

51. The hadrons are generally unstable particles and they continue to decay until they finally eject either one of a stable collection of particles, called baryons or mesons. The stable particles are the proton, photon, electron and the neutrino; the last two are called leptons; the photon is a gauge boson; and the proton is called a baryon.

52. If the particles remaining – at the end of a sequence of decay steps – contain a proton, the initial hadron is referred to as a baryon (which includes a single proton). If the particles remaining – at the end of the decay steps – contain only leptons and photons, the initial hadron is referred to as a meson.[iii]

57

4.10 Pair Production

53. When a positron and an electron are simultaneously ejected from an atom by a gamma ray photon, the event is called pair production. The action has been assumed to be the conversion of electromagnetic energy into matter, but there has been no explanation on how this is achieved.

54. One possible explanation is to assume that the atom has reached a conditionally stable state, and is about to eject matter in order to reach a lower energy level for greater stability. This implies that two or three electrons are in conjunction in their orbits and can be readily ejected to achieve a lower overall energy level for the atom. If a gamma ray photon has a minimum energy of 1.02MeV it will eject two of these as Auger electrons★. One of them will emerge from the atom as an electron; the other will be attracted towards the nucleus and be captured by a proton. The proton will therefore change to a neutron and immediately eject a positron and a neutrino; (the neutrino will generally not leave a trace in a cloud or bubble chamber because it has zero electric charge). Photographs also show no trace of a displaced, excited atom, thus confirming that the gamma ray energy has been completely absorbed and that both electrons have come from the same atom.

55. ★If both electrons are in orbital positions where little force is required to dislodge them, that force will be just greater than an electron's mass, i.e. $F = m \times$ (radial-acceleration) will be just greater than m, if the radial-acceleration is above 1 m/sec^2. Any force greater than this minimum will produce greater acceleration and a consequent increased kinetic energy – equally – to both electrons.

56. The simultaneous ejection of both positive and

negative electrons is due to a natural law, which requires there to be a conservation of electric charge in any collision between particles. The gamma ray photon has zero electric charge, hence the atom will eject both an electron and a positron to fulfil the natural law.

4.11   Resonance between Particles

57. The familiar phenomenon of resonance can occur in electrical systems when a sinusoidally varying voltage, of variable frequency, is applied to a series circuit comprising an inductance, capacitance and resistance. As the frequency is varied the current oscillations will pass through a peak at the resonance frequency. An analogous situation occurs in a mechanical system when a cyclically varying force − of constant amplitude − is applied to a mass, which is attached to a spring, and there is a constant friction-force against the movement of the mass. The sinusoidally varying displacement of the mass reaches a maximum for a specific frequency of the applied force.

58. At the nuclear level there are elementary particles (protons and neutrons), which consist of small, charged masses (quarks) in orbits around a central mass; the combined system being under the dynamic control of electromagnetic, centrifugal and strong gravitational forces. The small masses would achieve large radial oscillations, due to the frequent bombardment by external energetic particles, were it not for the damping effect of gluons. The ether of unit mass particles transmits the gluons − which are shock waves and their reflections − between the quarks and their central mass; and between the nucleons (protons and neutrons). The gluons therefore effectively stabilise the atom.

59. Another type of resonance also occurs at the elementary particle level, when two particles fleetingly share their dynamic systems; i.e. their central masses approach each other on near collision courses and form a strong gravitational bond. The orbits of their quarks consequently overlap (although probably not in the same plane), and the combined system is generally in an oscillatory, unstable condition, with the gluons providing a damping control. The original two particles eventually become separated after an extremely short period; but the time during which the two particles are linked together is called a resonance.

60. Such resonances, which have life-times of the same order as other unstable elementary particles, are now recognised as new forms of the latter. An example is the Δ^{++} particle, which is formed as a resonance in the near collision between a proton and a pi^+ particle.

4.12 Bending of a Light Ray near to a Star

61. Although the fundamental particles of unit mass, unit charge and unit pole are normally isolated, independent entities, it is possible that unit charges can become strongly bonded to unit mass particles – or elementary mass particles – in a strong gravitational field. Once the bond has been made it is only broken when a unit mass or an elementary particle moves out of the influence of a strong gravitational field, or the elementary particle is shattered by bombardment. For example, the quarks must be formed under the influence of the strong force from small fragments of mass (from particle collisions or bombardments), and acquire their electric charges – extremely rapidly – within the influence of a strong force

field. There may also exist briefly the small charged particles that emit gamma waves, which are due to the oscillatory movements of their unit charges after an impact in a strong force field.

62. The electromagnetic waves of a light ray, when it passes close to a star, are within the influence of a strong gravitational field, and are passing what are either unit mass particles or possibly small agglomerations of unit mass particles. The unit charges of the photons in the light ray can therefore become attached to the unit or resultant small masses, which are being attracted towards the large mass of the star. Energy is consequently lost from the light ray, whose frequencies are therefore subject to a red shift, and the direction of the ray undergoes a small deflection towards the star.

4.13 The Source of Energy and of Fundamental Particles

63. It has long puzzled mankind how the universe was created, and who the supreme being must be that started the creation process. As time has progressed the great complexity of every aspect of the evolution process, which affects both living matter/organisms and inanimate matter, has been gradually revealed by scientific study.

64. Today mankind is a little nearer to answering some of the basic questions about the origin and evolution of the universe. For example there seems to be general agreement that the process started at a given point in both space and time. The obvious question must then be: "What existed before this time?" A speculative answer may be that an omnific ether existed before this time and still exists throughout all space in our universe; and beyond!

65. A further question would then be: "If the start of Creation was at some point in time, how far back from then did time exist?" Again a speculative answer would be that mankind has invented both the concept of time and its measurement in order to observe and predict the progress of physical events, such as the movement of planets in their orbits around the Sun. Time therefore is only relevant to the observable universe and has no counterpart in the omnific ether.

66. Moreover, if the omnific ether is the source of the created matter in our physical universe – and imbued it with life giving energy and its related forces – then such physical entities could not have been present in the same form, nor can they be present now, in the omnific ether. To summarise; where there is no physical matter there is no requirement for our concept of time to record the progress of events; and where there is no need for time there can be no physical matter as we perceive it.

67. If these speculations are feasible then two further questions must arise, viz.: "If no physical matter ever existed, or exists, in the omnific ether, then will mankind ever be able to discover its presence?"; and "Will mankind ever know the process for the awesome energy of Creation?" (e.g. how are unit mass, unit charge and unit pole particles made in prodigious quantities). The answers to these questions depend upon the results of scientific research in the future.

References

(i)   *Options in Physics: Nuclear Physics*. Joyce Dacre, Heinemann Educational Books.

(ii) *Quarks, The Stuff of Matter*. Harald Fritzsch, Penguin Books.

(iii) *From Atoms to Quarks.* James S. Trefil, Athlone Press.

(iv) *Introduction to Atomic and Nuclear Physics.* Henry Semat, Rinehart.

(v) *The Particle Explosion.* Frank Close, Michael Marten, and Christine Sutton. Oxford University Press.

Further reading

The Nature of Matter. Edited by J.H. Mulvey, Clarendon Press.

The Cosmic Onion. F.E. Close, Heinemann Educational.

Oxford Dictionary of Science. O.U.P.